The Beat of Heart Stones
by Linda Cracknell

best foot books

First published by
Best Foot Books
P O Box 7512
Aberfeldy
PH15 2WX
ISBN Number: 978-0-9562453-1-1
July 2010

Cover Photo and illustrations by the author
Design and layout by embgraphics.co.uk
Printed by Short Run Press

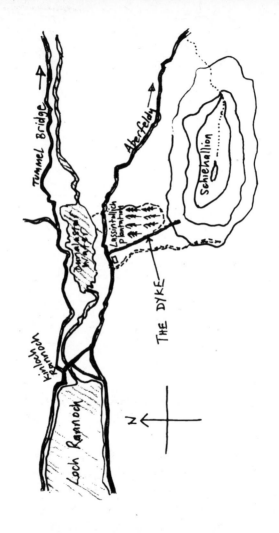

The Beat of Heart Stones

My heart's heaving as I climb from the road.
I'm like a diver, seeking upwards towards a
blue miasma – the membrane where freezing
fog thins.

I surface into sparkle, stop to gasp mouthfuls of
cut glass air. Feathers of ice float down onto my
hot face and hands as they moult from thawing
birch branches.

Hands on its grating rock, I lean back against
the dyke whose line keens up the hillside
ahead. The stone, silvery in this winter
sunlight, plants a ton into the ground with each
yard of advance. Its start is humid, kept damp
by the dark plantation squeezing in from its far
side. Bright moss blankets its foundations and
crawls across the protruding through-stones. I
can't hear much above the blood pulsing in my
ears. But could that have been a sigh?

I've my breath back now, so I'll go on, follow
the summoning line, the dyke's unswerving
strike towards the summit of Schiehallion.
One and a half miles. An insistent twenty six
degrees, South-South-East.

Twenty seven.

Sorry?
Silence.
Not even an utter of wind today.

Here, beyond the trees, they chose a different
type of rock – black and plate-thin rather than
square and glittering grey. As if it hasn't seen
the light for years.

Six.

Eh?

Hundred.

A yawn?

Million.

Did you speak?

Six hundred million years ago…

What?

… you'd have needed your snorkel.

A snorkel?

nguhhh

Did I wake you?

A deep-sea dive, it would have taken, to witness the beginnings of that stone you touch. Before it joined this scaly mosaic on the hill.

You were underwater?

The part of me you put your hand on now was a forest of sea lilies then, wafting their tendrils in the currents.

Oh.

Limestone. Dug from that hollow over there.
The scar's grassed over now. It's only a patch,
an outcrop, floated down from the limestone
pavements.

And are you limestone the rest of the way?

I'm the earth turned inside out – a display of what
ever's under the turf.

I see.

You don't want to find out for yourself?
To walk with me.

Of course. It's a beautiful day. I've my breath
back. Two or three hours to spare.

Huh.

So they used whatever was close by? Here's a block of quartz, the glitter of mica schist. Here a seaweed green section, here bare grey.

What the Earth spits out. Would you want to heave it far across the hills? You don't look very strong.

Looks can be…

It was weans and women and tinkers hauled these rocks — left them in a rickle each side of the line, within reach of the hands that built my long slow uphill spine.

Whose hands?

One craftsman each side. Raising two inward-leaning walls that kissed just before they were capped. Think of the men as you walk.

I am.

Quick-handed, with eyes sharpened for measuring.
They saw at a glance how one stone would nudge
and slide against another, the shape and ache of a
gap.

I see that. Your footstones are square blocks;
straight-edged. But here, halfway up, is an
L-shaped rock, waves caught in its texture.
It must have taken two to lift into place.
And small flat rocks pack against its non-
conforming curves, insist again on the
horizontal.

They made it a rule – never pick up a stone more
than once. Assess them where they lie.

A waste of effort?

If you're being paid by the yard.

What kind of men were they?

Fat-fingered.

With black thumbnails?

As they worked, memories of their great-great-grandfathers swung their thoughts over their shoulders. Ancestors with the same blackened thumbnails. Your fingers look slim and weak.

Look how I stride along next to you though, as you ride the waves of the land. Why don't you go around these hillocks? You seem sinuous enough for a detour.

I'm a march boundary.

Following a line older than yourself?

The natural push upwards of bed rock. That's what I rest on. The definition between lands and estates over the centuries.

Why a wall?

Oh, disputes leaving blood pooled on rock. Beasts to keep in. Or out. The usual things that spread a web of stone lines 500,000 miles across this island.

I see trails are worn in the earth by your side. So I'm not the first here. Whose beat am I following?

Come back in the dark and you'll see how they all use me as a corridor, the four-footed ones – wood mice, voles, hares – sheltering from the owls, making their chambers inside me. They treat me as a larder too. The fox slinking alongside me for his supper.

The rabbit I suppose?

Have you not seen my smoots – the rabbit-sized doorways they built through me?

That's very kind-hearted. A design to allow rabbits through.
Careful. That laughter's shuddering your coping stones. You'll lose even more of them.

I've no intention of losing them.

They look vulnerable, that's all, at that angle,
like leaning book spines on a shelf. One or two
have already tumbled, especially where the
trees have snatched at them. In places your
ridge is a mountain range, the surviving coping
stones like free-standing pinnacles.

Huh.

What were the smoots for then? I obviously got
the 'kindness' wrong.

*Kind to the hungry man perhaps – the one who
opened the trap door on my other side and pulled
out his dinner by its ears.*

Of course.

*Aye, you're in the tracks of the rabbit-lifter. And
the man who comes once a year to join me for a
promenade. He notes the topples and sags, where to
send the dyker in for repairs.*

9

You need attention each year?

Pah! I can stand tall for a hundred and fifty without a human touch.

Of course.
Although, with respect, you haven't.
When was he last here – your promenade
partner?

A blink ago. Perhaps forty years. Or fifty. It's got quiet. In the old days I had that many human hands on me.

And now?

The likes of you. The odd walker who's lost the path.

I came on purpose.

Scientists sampling my lichens.

You're certainly colourful; garish almost.
As though you've gone rusty in the rain, or
someone's dabbed you with fluorescent green
paint, or fine white corals have fastened in

your grooves and contours. This rosette prints
a stranded jelly-fish. Here, leopard spots of
black on orange. My fingertips – OK I admit
they're soft – pick up antique lace, porcelain.
And sunlight on the grain of the rock draws the
lines of an old man's face. How does it feel to
be so many things at once?

*You've overlooked my best mosses by staying on
the sunny side. 'Unique', they mutter, the ones
who come with magnifying glasses and scrape into
sample bottles. Lean over, take a look.*

Your dark side. I see the mole-coat that grows
over your stones.

*You can lean on me a little more. Use your hands
and feet.*

Really? God, that's gross.

What?

Something lurid as orange peel's growing over the most shadowed faces.

You're easily put off.

And you're going down this gully now? A kink of your spine over a knoll, a plunge downwards, and then you curl out again, tapering and expanding your vertebrae. And at your steepest section, the stones still run horizontal to the hill, and, oh … it's OK, I'm OK.

Slippery?

How do you stay so solid?

I have a heart.

Having a heart makes you solid? I've one too.

That, and this deep downward longing that holds me to the Earth.

Gosh - a heart and longing, you almost sound human. And you, so close to the Heart of Scotland!

Tell me, what makes up a dyke's heart?

Muscles and blood vessels.

No!

A joke.

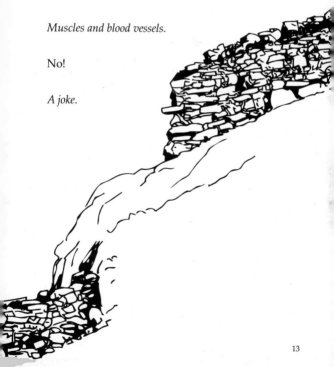

Ah, yes. Stones, I suppose.

*Small ones, packed carefully to hold my two walls
away from each other, to compose the still, strong
places of my inner life. The places that began as
secret and that I surrender over time.*

What do you mean?

See this sag in me here – this collapsing inwards?

It takes you off your true course.
You're like an eel in a burn.

*Wheesht, they'd be angry if they heard that, my
makers. Not quite, not yet that bad. A bit of settling
doesn't undermine me.*

What then?

*Where the moles have vibrated the earth around me,
loosening stones. Where the snow has squeezed its
way into the gaps under my capstones. Freeze, thaw,
freeze, thaw. Together they've shuggled my heart-
stones downwards. Then in have crept the mice
and voles, the adders slithered in to hibernate, the*

squirrels found their places to hoard winter feasts.
Snails, spiders, you name for me who hasn't nestled
in. And with the small inner stones pushed down so
low, my walls have sunk inwards, squeezing their
weight towards each other where my heart should be.

It sounds like your heart's alive.

And yours is dead?

I'm human.

And that speaks for itself?

Look!

You expect me to look?

A pure white stoat.

I feel it though.

It just poked its head out, and bobbed back.

Your noise scuttered it away. Follow me uphill, it'll
pop out again further up. I feel it wriggling through

my soul, running through my heart, where it hides
and hunts.

Doesn't it hurt?

*Paws on me, skin, suckers, roots. Inside, outside.
Hands on me. That's what I am. You all put your
prints on me and I carry their impression, outlive
them.*
Just think of the festival of my creation.

Those men with the measuring eyes and black
thumbnails?

*Them and the tinkers, camped up against
me each night wherever they stopped
work. Their horses, who dragged
the stone, grazing on their
hobbles. It took them
time to*

travel my whole length. You're only about halfway.

I think I need a sandwich.

*Put your hand inside me, and you'll find the bottles
the two dykers left at the end of each day rather
than carry them down again.
Eight yards between them.*

You must have looked so fine when you were
first built.

*An eyesore they said. Soil-smeared rock. An
infringement on the landscape, an insult to the eye.
And the ground on each side of me left sparkling
with the shards of trimmed stone. Like elf-arrows,
they said, and kept away.*

And now look at you.

The rain and wind soon bared me, but the fine

lichen has taken its time at the gilding.

You blend in so well.

My downfall perhaps.

Oh?

There's not many admire me enough, notice me enough, to help me stand.

Not the farmers?

It's cheaper to stretch wire across stakes. Look at me and you'll know the state of farming. A decline, and my collapse begins. This time I may never get up again.

But that's terrible. So your enemies are the moles and the ice. What about the trees?

All of them collude with the pull of the Earth, that longing I spoke of. The wind-tossed, unruly branches begin something, jostle my capstones. Then come the leaping deer scraping sharp hooves over me. They beat their way back and forth across

the hill where they spy weakness, an opportunity to
pass.

Has the sadness stopped you in your tracks?
Perhaps you'll lift my scattered stones, then.

I don't know how.

Try.

Well. Perhaps this one. Could go here. Oh, too
big. Or this one? No, sorry. Maybe this one.

You're right.

What?

You don't know how.

I'll walk you anyway. It's a kind of homage.

Huh.

Not impressed?
Silence then.
Just marching.

The open moor now. How strange that on one side of you the heather tangles darkly. On the other, just flat plains of grass.
No explanation to offer me?

And now the steep north face of the summit looms above us, spreading its shadow so that ice stars spar from the mosses at midday, blind to the sun. The ground as hard as you are. Despite the shade though, I can see how you continue to climb, a pale grey line. Are you crazy? What are you doing right up there?

I knew you wouldn't be up to it.

Found your voice again, then. Wouldn't be up to what?

The climb.

Did I say I wasn't continuing?

You look weary.

And you're a good foot shorter than you've been until now.

Why do you think that is?

No stone available?

On a Scottish hillside?

Tell me.

Listen to your feet.

The suck of bog. Where its not frozen.

Exactly. Less height equals less weight.

And up here. Somewhere.

Take it slowly, now. You're panting, not making sense.

On. The North side. Maskelyne's Observatory.

That he burnt down, in the end.

Were you here then? Did you witness it?

I was built just a little after. Maskelyne was based

east of here, but the ground still remembered.
Rumours whistled through the shoots of heather,
there was a lingering scent of scorched grass. After
seventeen weeks up here with his plumb-line,
telescopes and wine in the worst summer that had
ever been known, the end, they said, was in fiddle
music and whisky and fire. A blaze of a farewell
party.

The weight of the Earth, the 'attraction of
mountains', his experiment. And. It gave us.
Contours. To help us visualise the steepness of
this land.

The hill's ripples. Marked on the map you insist on
carrying. As if you could get lost, walking with me.

You're a reliable guide, at least so far.

Take a break. Lean on me if you wish, eat your
sandwich. What's the rush, now you've woken me
anyway. Stay longer.

I've a friend to meet. And you've become
tiresomely steep, joined forces with the burn,
gurgling under your stones. Doesn't it bother you?

Water. And Rock. Give and take.

Oh, and now finally, I see where you meet the
head-dyke. And the cairn, on Cnoc na h-Iolaire.

Where they celebrated.

What?

The two dykes, two teams meeting.

I wonder if they had views like this – could
pick out the whale-back of Ben Nevis over
there, the spikes of the Mamores, Ben Alder's
snow-filled eastern corries. At that time I
suppose Dun Alastair would have been a
swampy river, crowded with birch and alder,
not yet flooded for the hydro.

You think that's the only change I've seen?

Tell me.

The tickle of bere growing up against me in the Spring.

Bere?

Ninety-day barley.

Grown way up here?

Where else was dry enough? I don't miss the wild goats and their head butts. The milkmaids, yes. Their song each day chittering along my coping stones as they climbed to the cattle. Over the years the song trickled through the gaps, into my heart. So many once lived and worked amongst these hills and whispered their stories and secrets against me. I've breathed them in, stored them in the crevices between stone and air, where I keep my dreams. They're there for anyone who'll listen closely enough.

Look at that, flying so low.

The gaps in me ache. I was about to tell you, but you're easily distracted.

Jets screaming through the glen. Way below us. And look! Above you, a microlite's circling the summit. It must make you proud, doesn't it? To be the biggest man-made structure on such a famous hill? The pilots must see you as a marker, the massive arm of a compass.

A monument, you might say.

All the thought that's circled Stonehenge, and the bringing of its rocks. Who puzzles over your tons of careful building?

Who indeed?

So, we carry on. Even above the head dyke you're still intent on climbing, maintaining your twenty six degrees?

25

Twenty seven.

All brave, I see, crossing the snow gully up there. Did the fairies keep pulling you towards the symmetry of the summit?

It's more of a human story, mine. Be brave yourself. Join me.

You look a little half-hearted now, broken and low.

Keep going.

And up there, you've collapsed into the grey scree that's tumbled from the summit. Are you not up to going beyond?

How can you tell, yet? Stay with me and you'll see. Tell me things. Or sing.

Are you afraid of Maskelyne's thing?

Afraid?

Of gravity.

That longing.

Your downfall. Look at me. I can keep going,
kick steps into the petrified snow, pull myself
up on heather stems, use a knee here or there.
I'm following the tripod prints of the hare.

Oh.

Sorry. I couldn't help knocking you. Your
stones are spreading out so, displaced from
vertical… and you've transformed, to salmon-
pink.

I can still speak

I don't think I can go up
any further.

I can still listen.

You haven't gone any further yourself. The
ground's so loose underfoot, there's no risk
of sheep getting around that way. The hill has
built its own defences.

We've climbed so high that half of Scotland
seems to unfold, the horizon dropped away
below us.

Hello?
Gone quiet on me.
Hello?
I need an easier way down. It's too steep your
way. I'll follow a contour, find the spur of the
hill. So then, I'll say…

Was that a sigh? A gurgle, as if you've gone
under. A sob, almost.

And so is your end just a sprawl, a scattering,
a meeting with the downward rattle of scree
that the hill has thrown over its shoulder?

Acknowledgements
Warm thanks go to David Fleming for walking whilst sharing his knowledge of dykeing; Claire Thomas for archaeological information; and Thomas Harley Deakin for initiating the design and layout of this book as part of an MLitt in Publishing Studies at The University of Stirling. Part of *The Beat of Heart Stones* was published in the Journal of the John Muir Trust, Spring 2009.

About the Author
Linda Cracknell's short fiction has been published in two collections: *Life Drawing* (2000) and *The Searching Glance* (2008). She also writes drama for BBC Radio 4, and is editor of a non-fiction anthology on the wild places of Britain and Ireland, *A Wilder Vein* (2009). She regularly takes walks with a pen in hand in pursuit of stories. The writing of *The Beat of Heart Stones* and a series of other walks was enabled by a Creative Scotland Award in 2007 (supported by the National Lottery through the Scottish Arts Council). She lives in Highland Perthshire.
http://walkingandwriting.blogspot.com